BIG AND SMALL

Colour the big picture and cross the small picture.

Date: ____________________

Teacher's Signature: ____________________

BIG AND SMALL

Write 'B' for Big and 'S' for small

Date: ________________

Teacher's Signature: ________________

UP AND DOWN

Colour the baby monkey which is 'UP' on the tree and circle the mummy monkey which is 'DOWN.

Date: ____________________ Teacher's Signature: ____________________

UP AND DOWN

Put a circle around the mangoes which are UP on the tree.

Count the mangoes in the basket and write the number in the given box.

Date: ____________

Teacher's Signature: ____________

IN AND OUT

Colour the fish 'IN' the net 'Red' and colour the fish 'OUT' of the net 'Blue'.

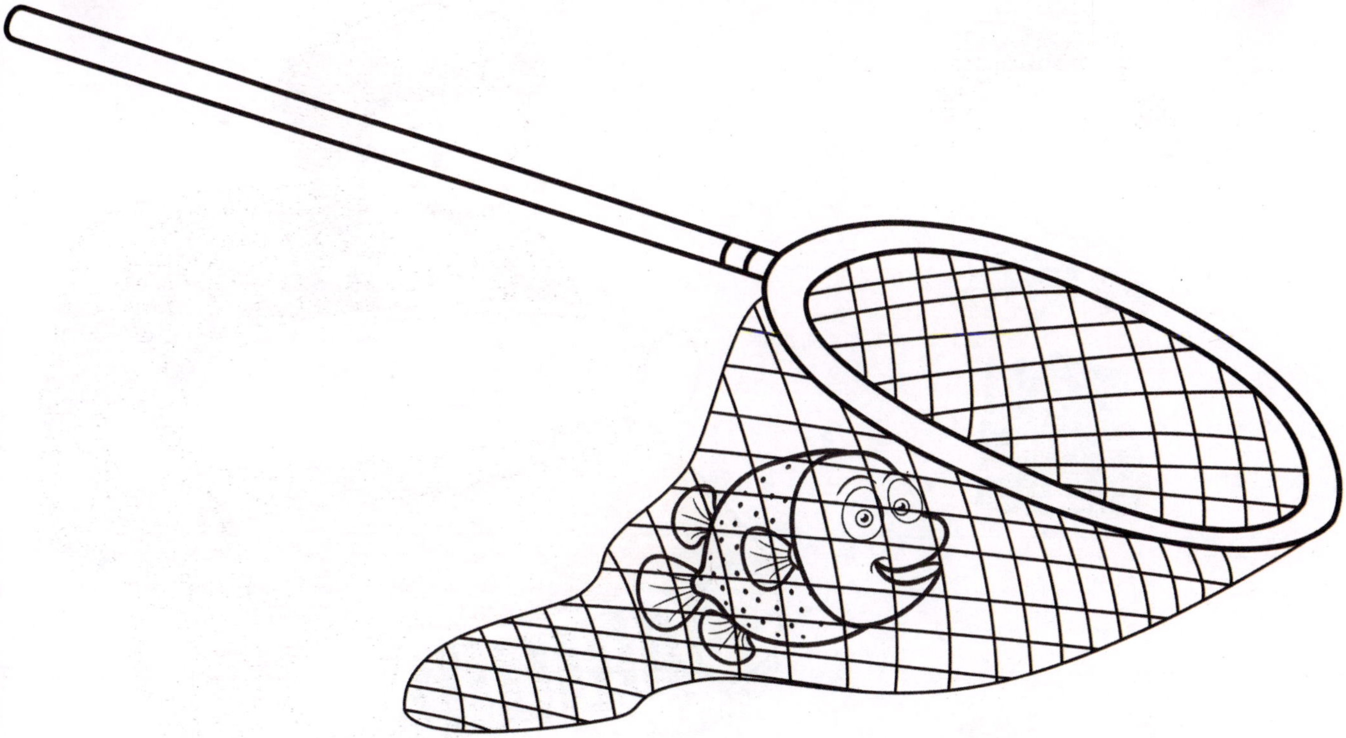

Date: ______________ Teacher's Signature: ______________

IN AND OUT

Write 'I' for the things which are Inside and 'O' for the things which are outside in the given pictures.

Date: ____________________ Teacher's Signature: ____________________

LONG AND SHORT

Colour the 'Long' string using blue colour and the 'Short' string using green colour.

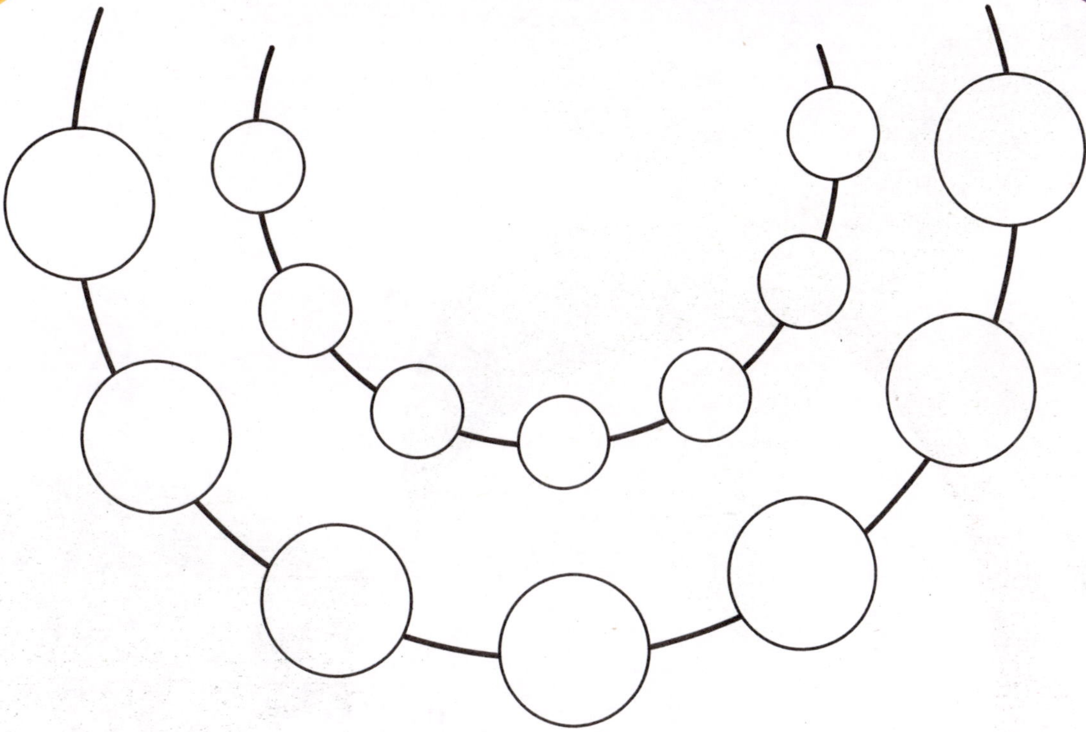

Colour the 'Long' train red and 'Short' train yellow.

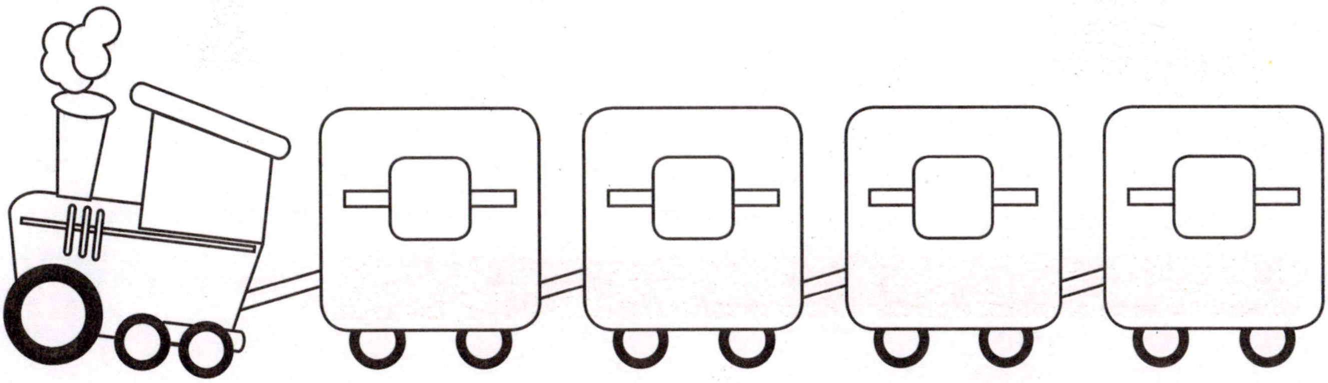

Date: ____________________

Teacher's Signature: ____________________

LONG AND SHORT

Write 'L' for long and 'S' for short.

Date: ________________

Teacher's Signature: ________________

THICK AND THIN

Tick (✓) the 'Thick' object and
Cross (×) the 'Thin' object.

Date: ________________ Teacher's Signature: ________________

THICK AND THIN

Colour the thick objects with brown crayon and the thin objects with blue crayon.

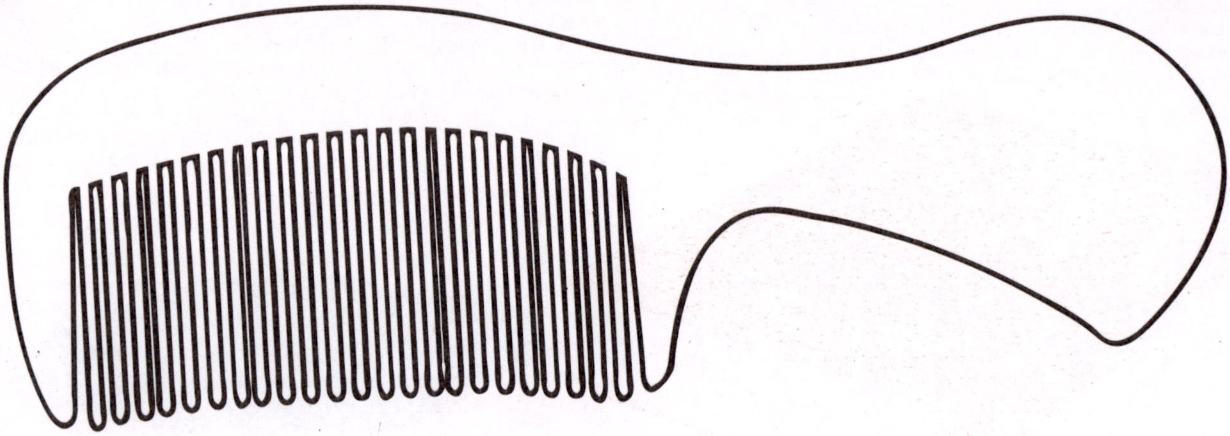

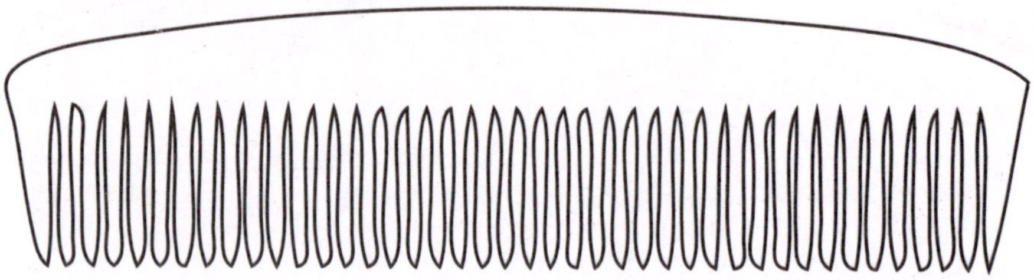

Date: ____________________ Teacher's Signature: ____________________

HEAVY AND LIGHT

Colour the heavy animal in 'Grey' colour and the light animal in 'Brown' colour.

Date: ____________________ Teacher's Signature: ____________________

HEAVY AND LIGHT

Write 'H' for heavy and 'L' for light objects.

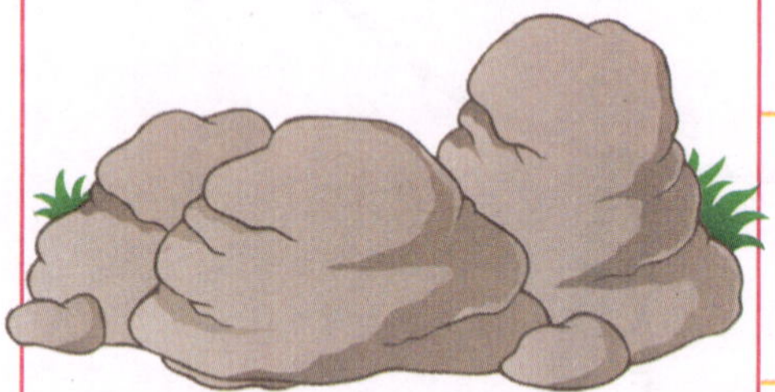

Date: ____________________

Teacher's Signature: ____________________

NEAR AND FAR

Colour the things which are 'NEAR' to the house and circle the things that are 'FAR' from the house.

Date: ________________

Teacher's Signature: ________________

NEAR AND FAR

Tick (✓) the objects which are near the hut and circle the objects which are far from the hut.

Date: ________________ Teacher's Signature: ________________

MATCHING

Join the shapes to the matching objects.

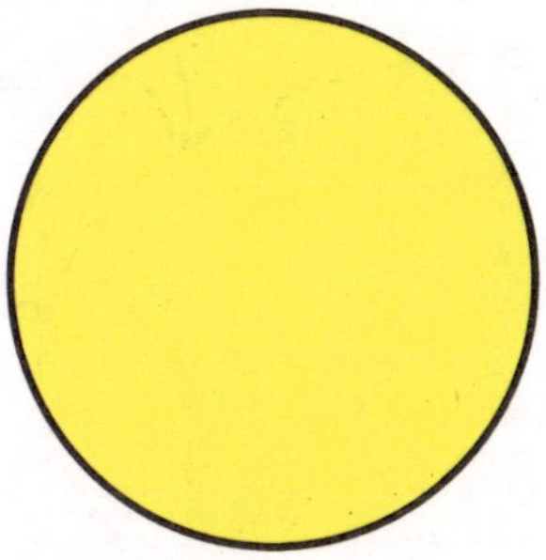

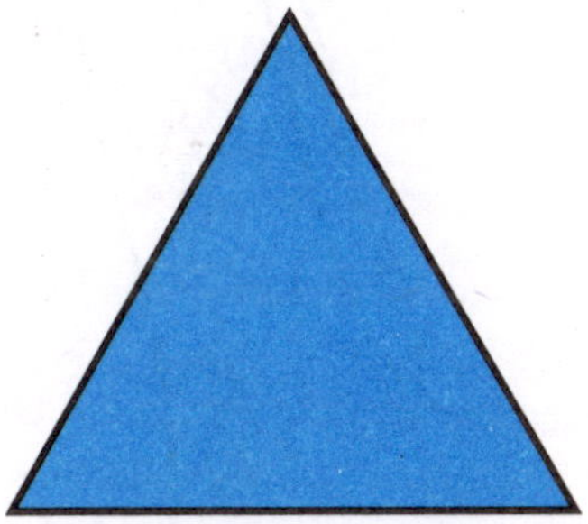

Date: ________________ Teacher's Signature: ________________

COLOURING FUN

Trace and colour all the oval shapes yellow.

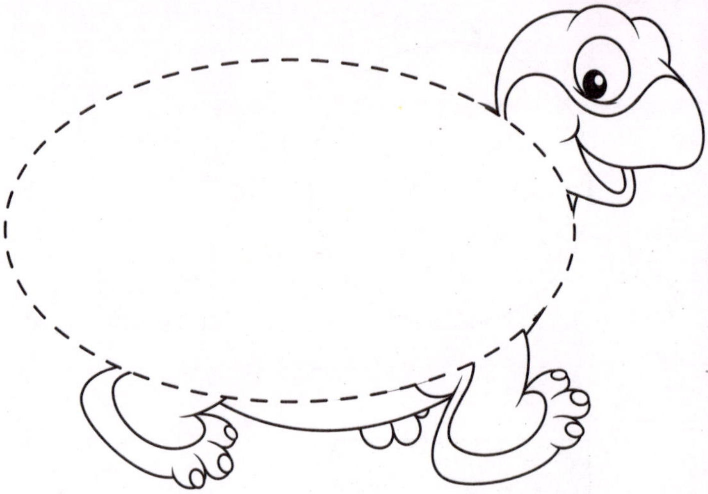

Date: ____________________ Teacher's Signature: ____________________

TRACE AND COLOUR

Trace and colour the circle shaped objects.

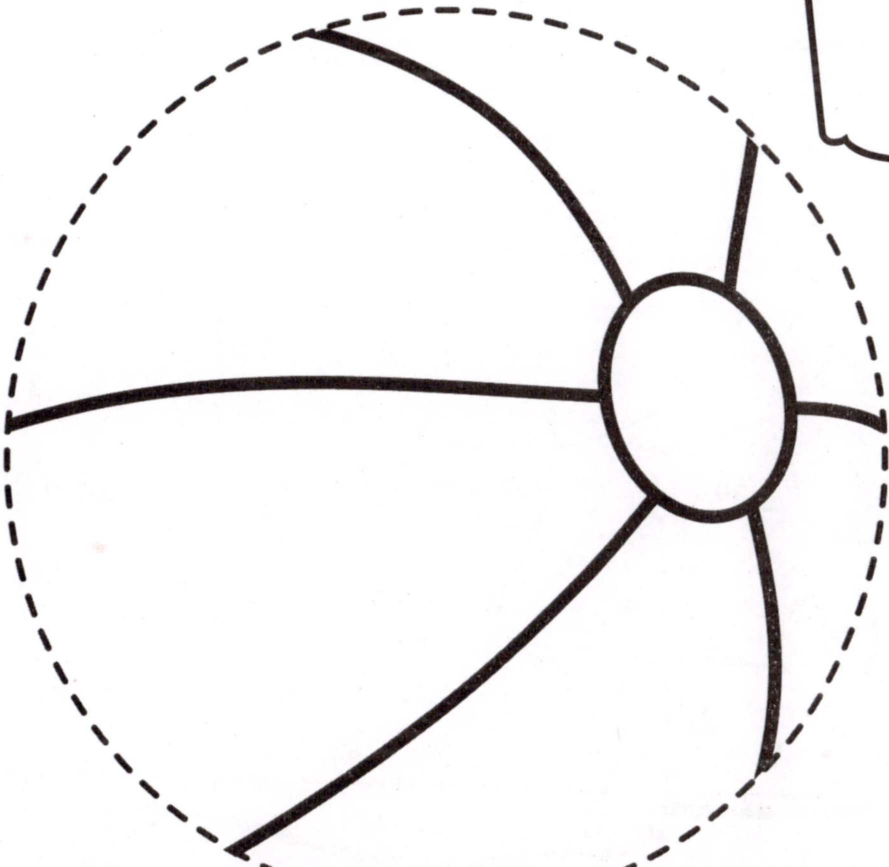

Date: ______________

Teacher's Signature: ______________

DOT TO DOT

Join the dots and colour the picture.

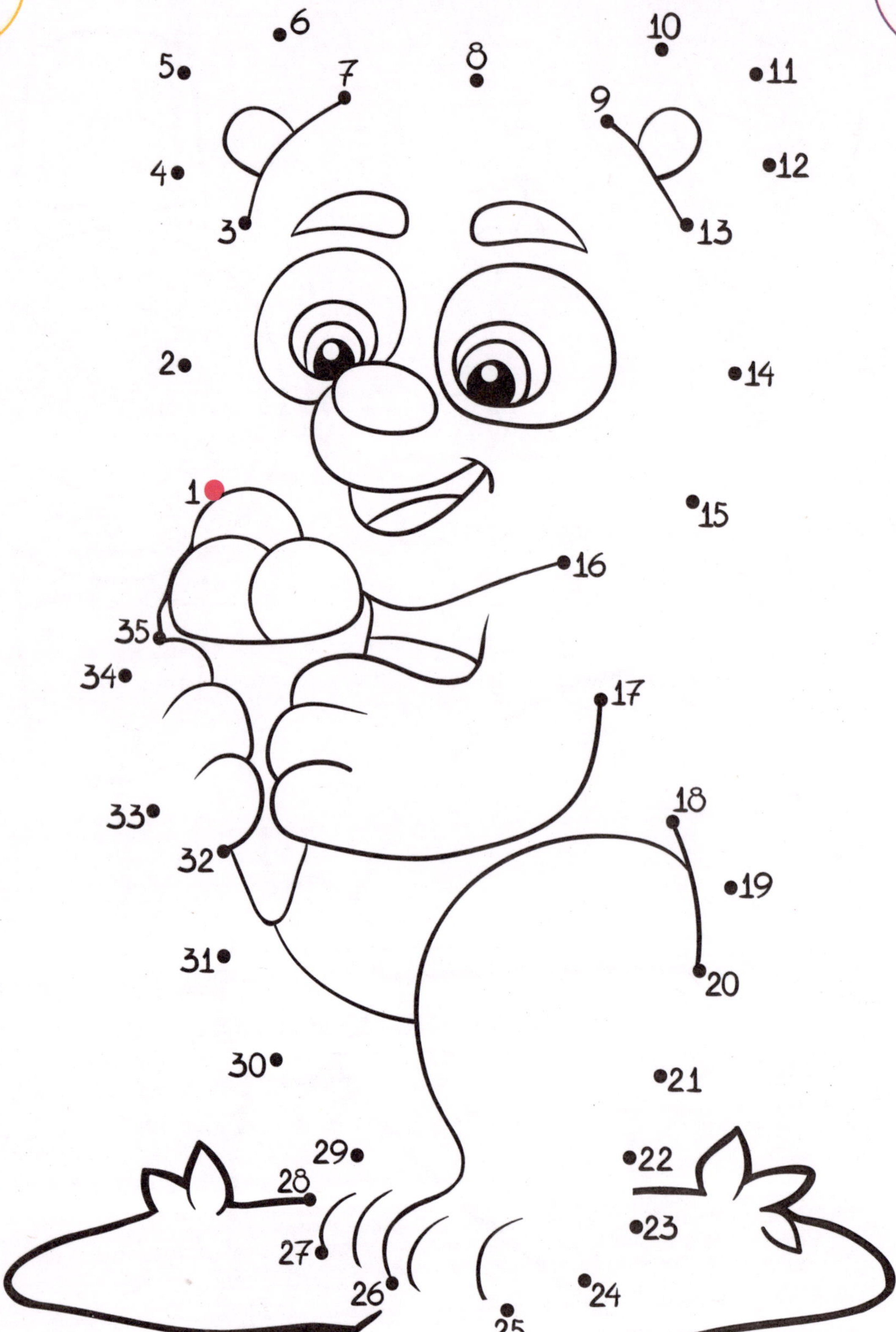

Date: ________________ Teacher's Signature: ________________

FIND AND TRACE

Find, trace and colour the hidden numbers.

Date: ____________________ Teacher's Signature: ____________________

ABACUS (0-9)

Draw the beads on the bars of abacus to show given number.

T O

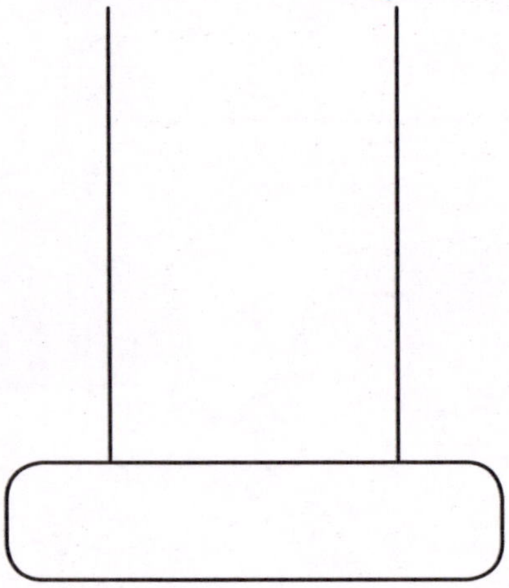

9

T O

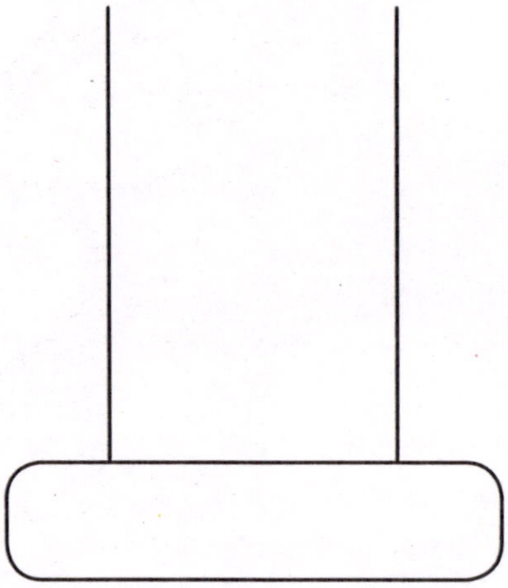

7

T O

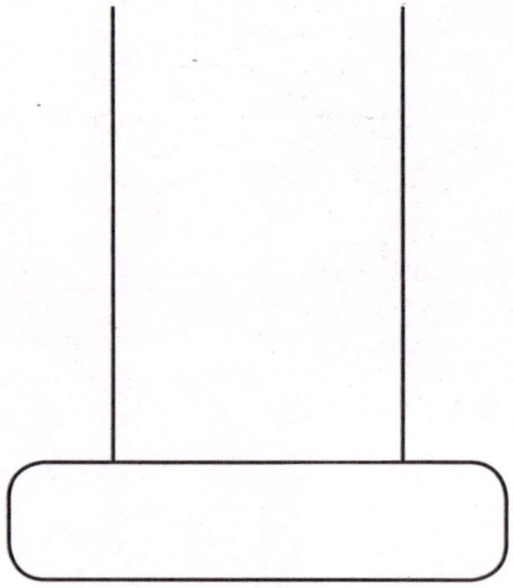

2

T O

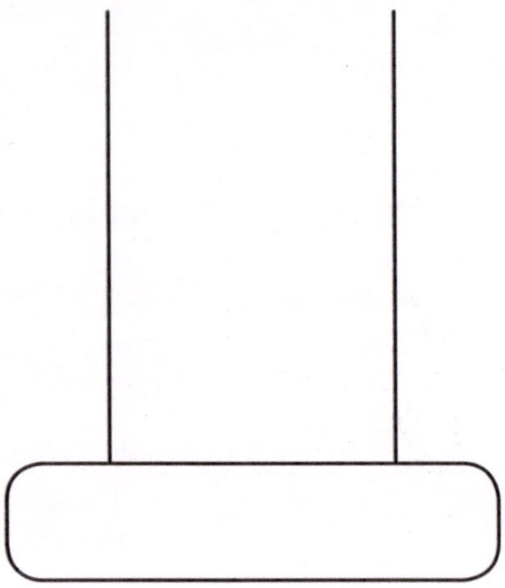

1

T O

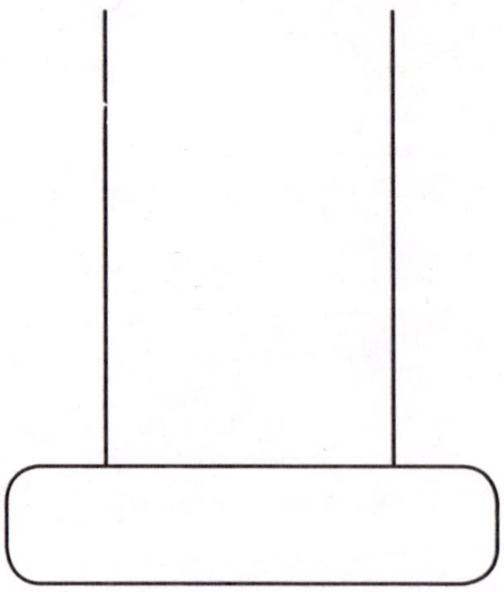

5

T O

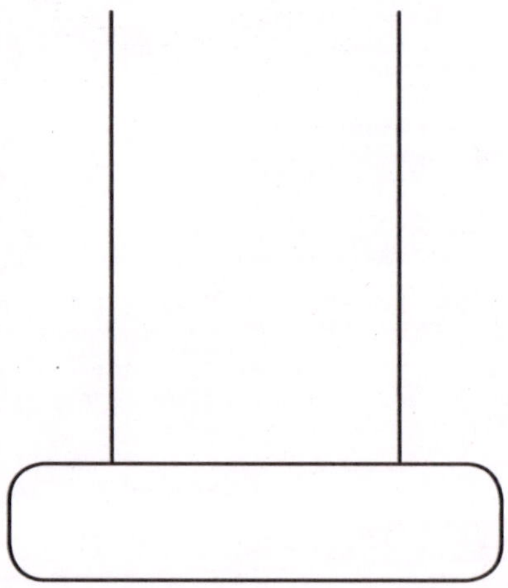

8

Date: ________________

Teacher's Signature: ________________

FORWARD COUNTING (0-9)

T	O
	0
	•
	•
	•
	•
	•
	•
	•
	•
	•

T	O
	0
	•
	•
	•
	•
	•
	•
	•
	•
	•

Date: ________________

Teacher's Signature: ________________

COUNT AND WRITE

Count the fruits in the basket and write the number in the given box.

Date: ______________

Teacher's Signature: ______________

WHAT COMES AFTER

Look the pictures given above and then draw the missing picture that comes after.

Date: ______________ Teacher's Signature: ______________

WHAT COMES AFTER (0-9)

Write the numbers that come after.

3		7	
0		5	
8		2	
4		6	
1		8	

Date: ____________________

Teacher's Signature: ____________________

WRITE FORWARD COUNTING (10-19)

T	O
1	0

T	O
1	0

Date: ____________________

Teacher's Signature: ____________________

FORWARD COUNTING (0 - 19)

Count and Fill in the missing numbers.

Date: ____________________ Teacher's Signature: ____________________

WHAT COMES AFTER (10-19)

Write the numbers that come after.

Number	After	Number	After
17		11	
10		13	
12		16	
14		10	
18		15	

Date: ____________________ Teacher's Signature: ____________________

MISSING NUMBERS (0-19)

Fill in the missing numbers in correct order.

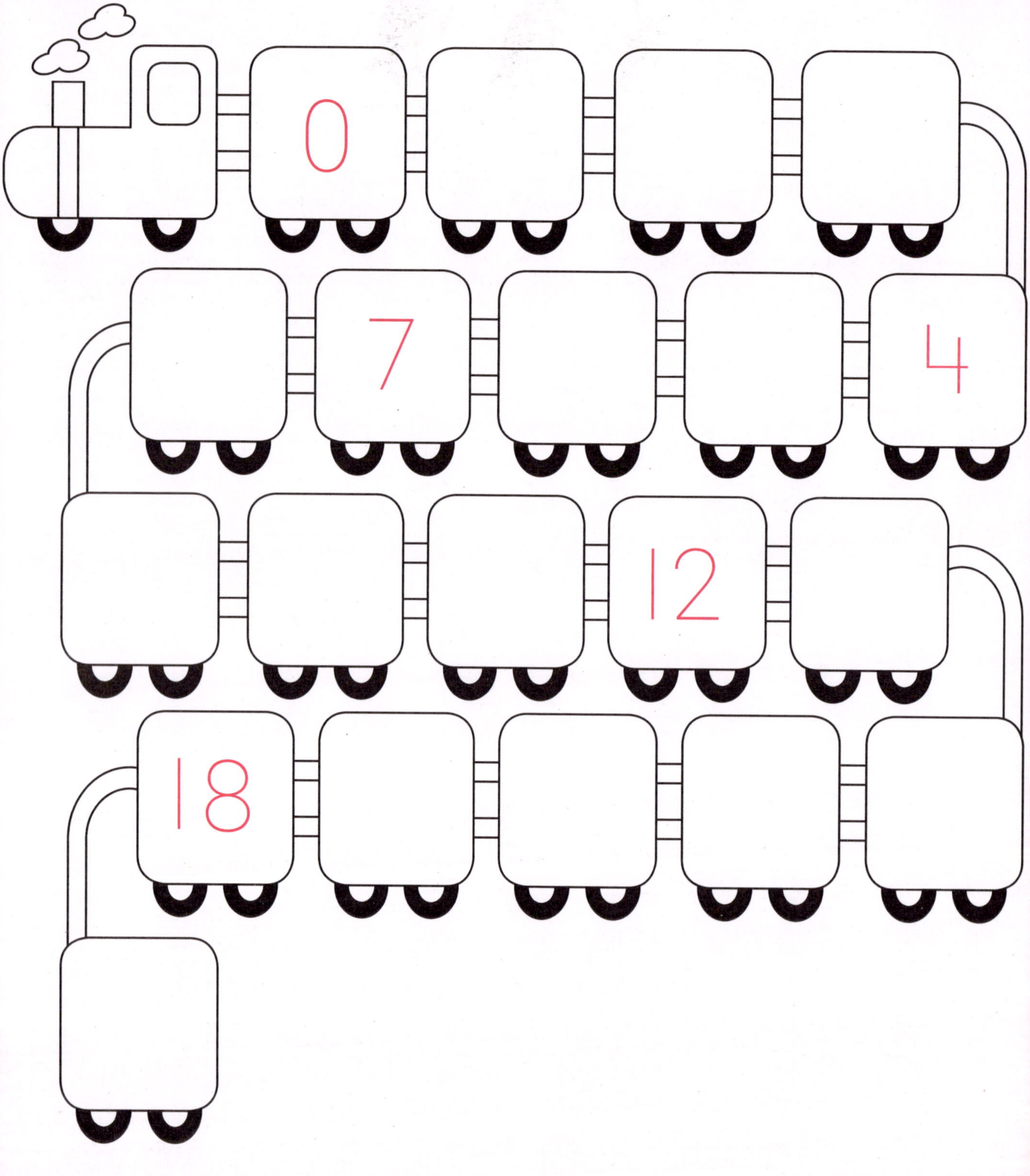

Date: ____________________ Teacher's Signature: ____________________

WHAT COMES IN-BETWEEN

Circle and colour the objects which are in between.

Write the numbers that comes in-between.

2		4		1		3
11		13		17		19
14		16		3		5

Date: ________________

Teacher's Signature: ________________

WHAT COMES IN BETWEEN (0-19)

T	O
1	4
	5
1	0
	7
1	2
	9
1	6
	3
	2
1	7

T	O

T	O
1	6
	7
1	2
	9
1	4
1	1
1	8
	5
	4
1	9

Date: ______________ Teacher's Signature: ______________

WRITE FORWARD COUNTING (20-29)

T	O
2	0

T	O
2	0

Date: ____________________

Teacher's Signature: ____________________

WRITE FORWARD COUNTING (0-29)

T	O
	0

T	O
1	0

T	O
2	0

Date: ________________ Teacher's Signature: ________________

WHAT COMES AFTER (20-29)

Write the numbers that come after.

Number	After	Number	After
21		20	
25		28	
22		26	
24		23	
27		26	

Date: ____________________

Teacher's Signature: ____________________

MISSING NUMBERS (20-29)

Fill in the missing numbers in correct order.

Date: ________________ Teacher's Signature: ________________

WRITE THE MISSING NUMBERS (0-29)

0			3	
		7		
10				14
	18		16	
		22		

Date: ______________

Teacher's Signature: ______________

WHAT COMES IN BETWEEN (0-29)

T	O
2	1
2	4
	7
1	9
2	0
	3
1	0
2	5
	2
1	3

T	O

T	O
2	3
2	6
	9
2	1
2	2
	5
1	2
2	7
	4
1	5

Date: ________________ Teacher's Signature: ________________

WRITE FORWARD COUNTING (30-39)

T	O
3	0

T	O
3	0

Date: ____________________ Teacher's Signature: ____________________

WRITE FORWARD COUNTING (0-39)

T	O	T	O	T	O	T	O
	0	1	0	2	0	3	0

Date: ____________________ Teacher's Signature: ____________________

WHAT COMES AFTER (30-39)

Write the numbers that come after.

Number	After	Number	After
32		30	
38		33	
34		36	
37		31	

Date: ________________ Teacher's Signature: ________________

MISSING NUMBERS

Fill in the missing numbers in correct order.

Date: ______________ Teacher's Signature: ______________

WHAT COMES IN BETWEEN (0-39)

T	O
3	7
2	2
3	0
	8
1	3
3	4
1	9
2	9
3	1
2	3

T	O

T	O
3	9
2	4
3	2
1	0
1	5
3	6
2	1
3	1
3	3
2	5

Date: ________________ Teacher's Signature: ________________

WHAT COMES BEFORE

Look the pictures given above and then draw the missing picture that comes before.

Date: ________________ Teacher's Signature: ________________

WRITE BACKWARD COUNTING (9 - 0)

T	O
	9

T	O
	9

T	O
	9

Date: ________________ Teacher's Signature: ________________

WHAT COMES BEFORE (0-9)

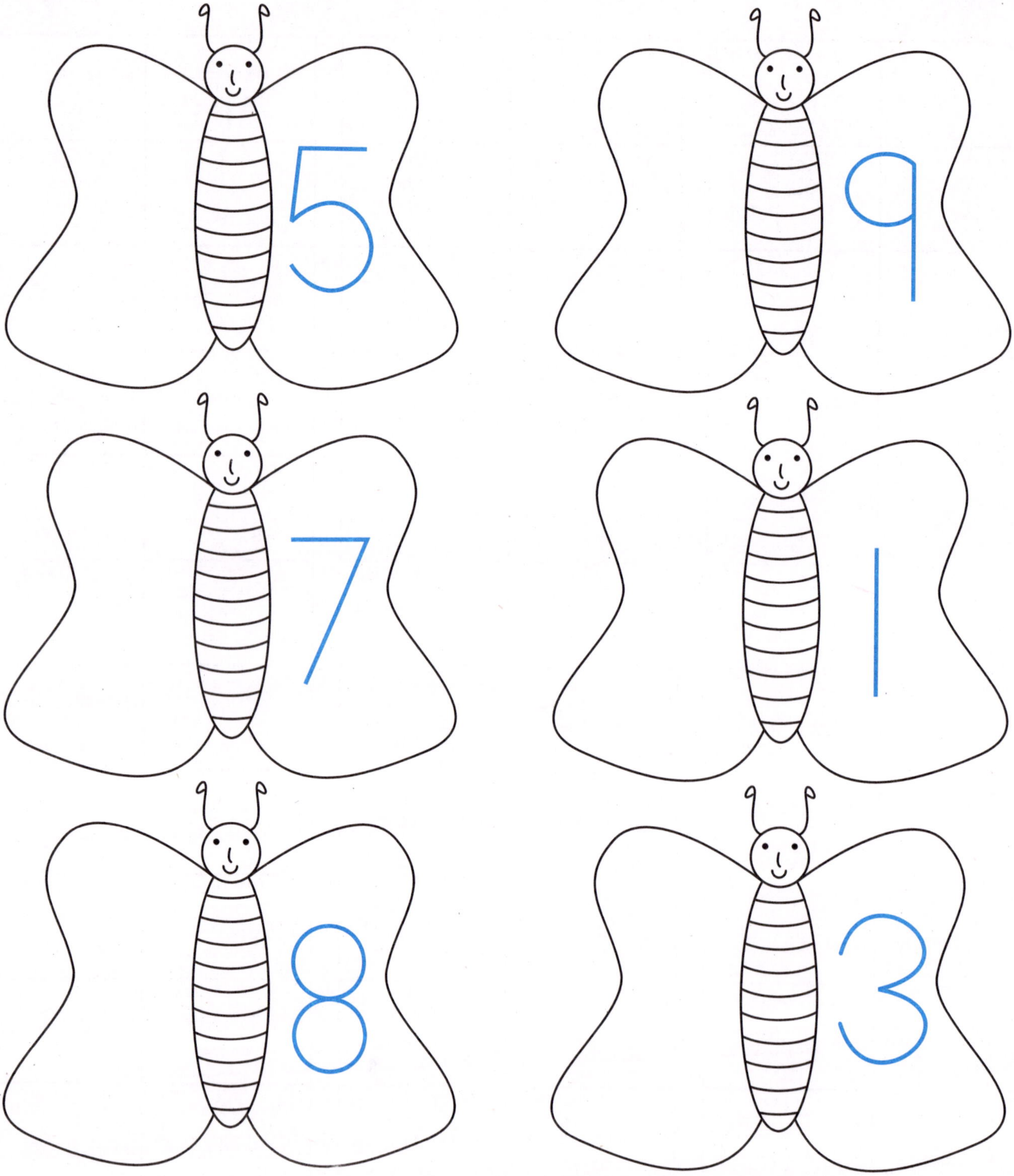

Date: ________________ Teacher's Signature: ________________

FORWARD COUNTING (40-49)

T	O
4	0

T	O
4	0

Date: ____________________ Teacher's Signature: ____________________

WHAT COMES AFTER (0-49)

Write the numbers that come after.

47		40	
21		32	
14		16	
38		23	

Date: ____________ Teacher's Signature: ____________

WHAT COMES IN BETWEEN (0-49)

T	O
4	4
2	8
3	9
2	0
4	7
	9
4	5
4	0
1	9
3	3

T	O

T	O
4	6
3	0
4	1
2	2
4	9
1	1
4	7
4	2
2	1
3	5

Date: ____________________

Teacher's Signature: ____________________

WRITE FORWARD COUNTING (0-47)

	0											

Date: ____________________ Teacher's Signature: ____________________

WRITE BACKWARD COUNTING (19-10)

T	O
1	9

T	O
1	9

Date: ____________________ Teacher's Signature: ____________________

WRITE BACKWARD COUNTING (19-0)

T	O
1	9

T	O
	9

Date: ____________________ Teacher's Signature: ____________________

WHAT COMES BEFORE (10-19)

Write the numbers that come before.

	11		17
	14		15
	18		19
	16		12

Date: ________________

Teacher's Signature: ________________

COLOUR

Colour the smallest object blue and biggest object green.

Date: ____________________

Teacher's Signature: ____________________

SMALLEST NUMBER (0 - 19)

Colour the petal in each flower with smallest number.

Date: ____________________

Teacher's Signature: ____________________

BIGGEST NUMBER (0-19)

Find the biggest number and draw a circle around it.

Date: ________________ Teacher's Signature: ________________

FORWARD COUNTING (50-59)

T	O
5	0

T	O
5	0

Date: ____________________

Teacher's Signature: ____________________

WRITE FORWARD COUNTING (50-59)

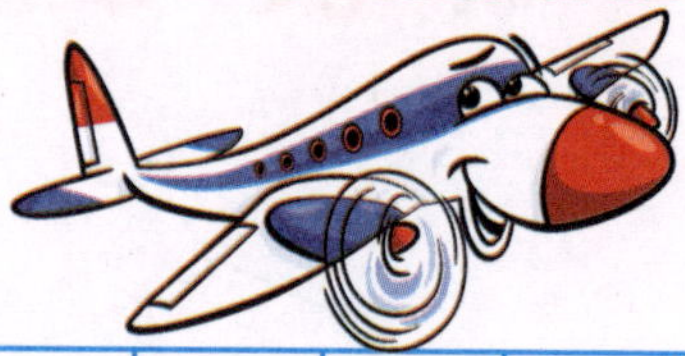

	50											

Date: ____________________ Teacher's Signature: ____________________

WHAT COMES AFTER (0-59)

Write the numbers that come after.

51		48	
54		50	
29		57	
33		15	

Date: ________________ Teacher's Signature: ________________

MISSING NUMBERS (0-59)

Write the missing numbers.

0			3						9
	11				15				
		22					27		
30				34					
						46			
			53				57		

Date: ________________ Teacher's Signature: ________________

WHAT COMES IN BETWEEN (0-59)

T	O
2	7
3	9
5	0
5	4
4	8

T	O

T	O
2	9
4	1
5	2
5	6
5	0

Date: ____________________

Teacher's Signature: ____________________

WRITE BACKWARD COUNTING (29-20)

T	O
2	9

T	O
2	9

Date: ____________________ Teacher's Signature: ____________________

WRITE BACKWARD COUNTING (29-0)

T	O
2	9

T	O
1	9

T	O
	9

Date: ________________ Teacher's Signature: ________________

WHAT COMES BEFORE (19-29)

	28		22
	20		24
	25		29
	23		27

Date: ____________________ Teacher's Signature: ____________________

GREATER THAN / LESS THAN / EQUAL TO > / = / <

Count and write the numbers, put the correct sign.

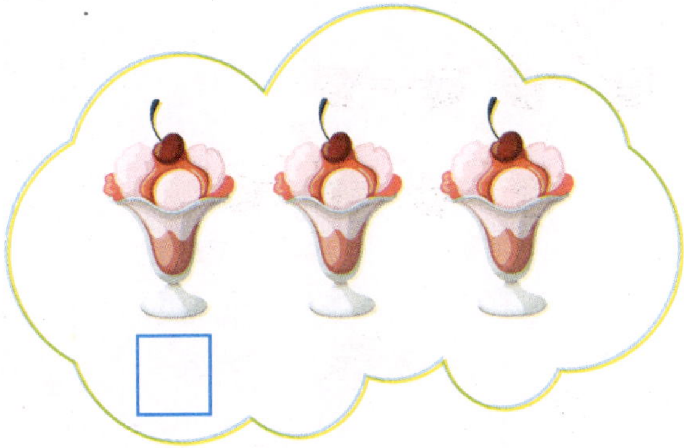

Date: ________________ Teacher's Signature: ________________

GREATER THAN / LESS THAN / EQUAL TO > / = / <

Count and write the numbers, put the correct sign.

Date: ____________________

Teacher's Signature: ____________________

BIGGEST NUMBER (0-39)

Colour the part of the kite that has the biggest number and write the number in the centre of each kite.

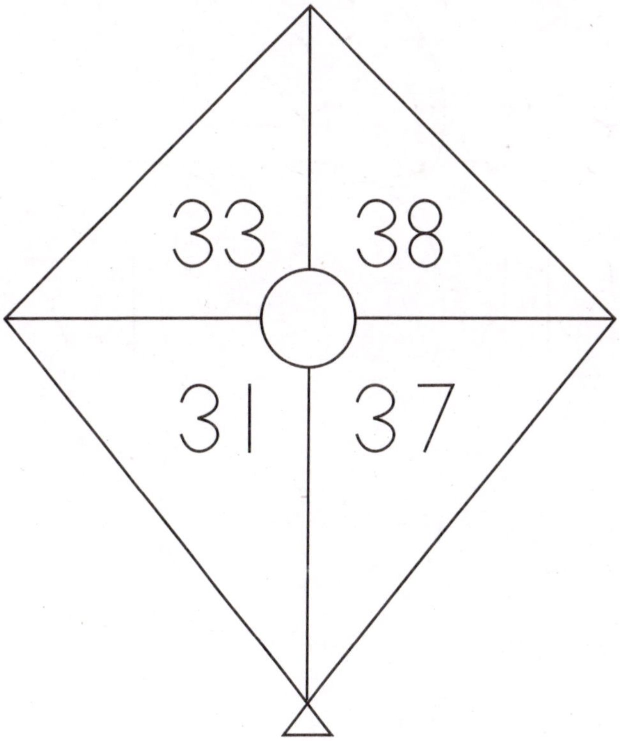

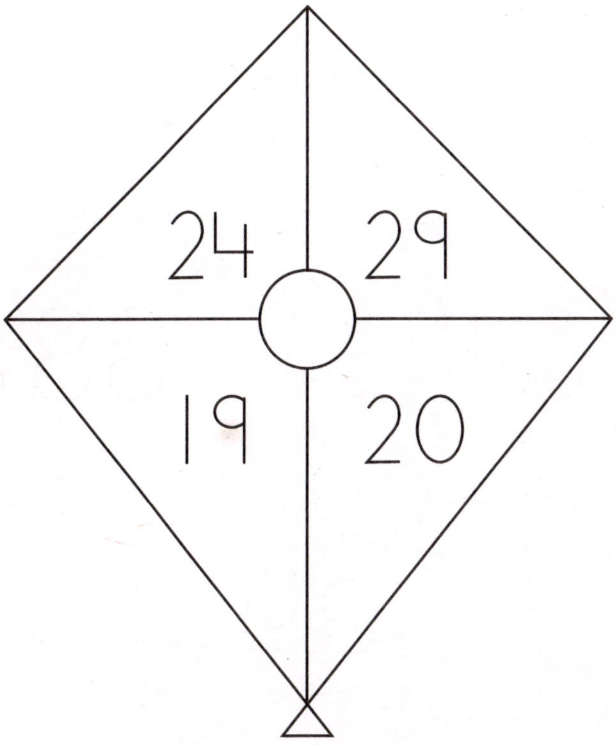

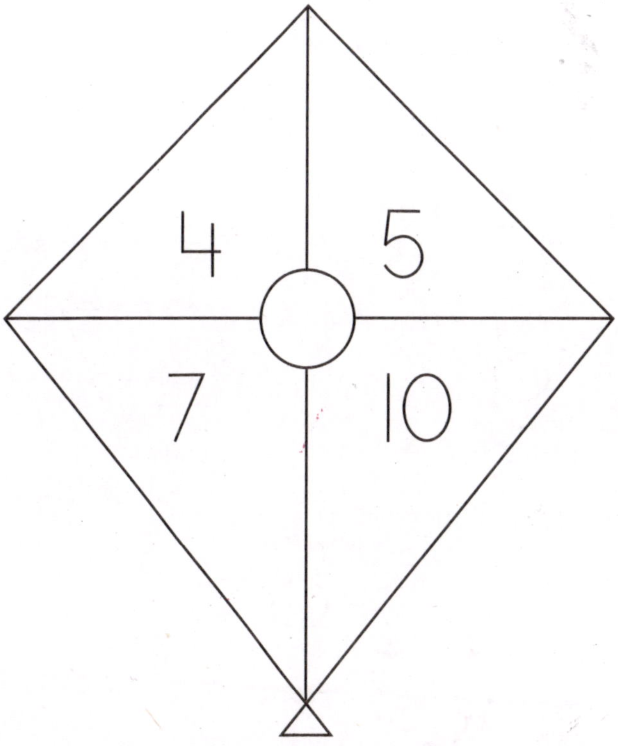

Date: ____________________ Teacher's Signature: ____________________

SMALLEST NUMBER (0-39)

Colour the part of the flower that has the smallest number and write the number in the centre of each flower.

Date: ________________ Teacher's Signature: ________________

WRITE FORWARD COUNTING (60-69)

T	O
6	0

T	O
6	0

Date: ____________________

Teacher's Signature: ____________________

WRITE FORWARD COUNTING (0-69)

0												

Date: ________________ Teacher's Signature: ________________

WHAT COMES AFTER (0-69)

Write the numbers that come after.

22		50	
34		68	
59		47	
61		35	

Date: ________________ Teacher's Signature: ________________

WHAT COMES IN BETWEEN (0-69)

T	O
2	7
4	4
3	9
5	0
6	2
1	6
	8
4	1
3	2
5	5

T	O

T	O
2	9
4	6
4	1
5	2
6	4
1	8
1	0
4	3
3	4
5	7

Date: ____________

Teacher's Signature: ____________

WRITE BACKWARD COUNTING (39-30)

T	O
3	9

T	O
3	9

Date: ____________________

Teacher's Signature: ____________________

WRITE BACKWARD COUNTING (39-0)

T	O	T	O	T	O	T	O
3	9	2	9	1	9		9

Date: ____________________ Teacher's Signature: ____________________

WHAT COMES BEFORE (30-39)

Write the numbers that come before.

	32		39
	38		34
	31		37
	36		35

Date: ______________

Teacher's Signature: ______________

PUT <, = ,> (0-59)

16	◯	12	45	◯	54
27	◯	27	41	◯	1
13	◯	31	19	◯	25
58	◯	48	33	◯	23
36	◯	24	17	◯	17
57	◯	59	4	◯	2

Date: ____________ Teacher's Signature: ____________

BIGGEST NUMBER

Circle the biggest number in each set.

41 8 50	5 25 52
37 42 33	51 58 50
16 12 9	19 24 29
10 50 20	69 62 22
9 4 7	23 27 21

Date: ______________ Teacher's Signature: ______________

BIGGEST NUMBER / SMALLEST NUMBER

Colour the biggest number with red crayon and smallest number with yellow crayon.

16, 18, 10, 9

49, 54, 50, 52

2, 8, 7, 9

7, 26, 36, 16

47, 42, 45, 41

21, 25, 15, 28

Date: ______________

Teacher's Signature: ______________

NUMBER NAME - ONE (1)

One				

Date: ____________________

Teacher's Signature: ____________________

NUMBER NAME - TWO (2)

Two				

Date: ________________ Teacher's Signature: ________________

WRITE FORWARD COUNTING (70-79)

T	O
7	0

T	O
7	0

Date: ________________

Teacher's Signature: ________________

WRITE FORWARD COUNTING (0-79)

0												

Date: ____________________

Teacher's Signature: ____________________

WHAT COMES AFTER (0-79)

Write the numbers that come after.

41		77	
75		12	
50		78	
26		33	

Date: ____________________ Teacher's Signature: ____________________

WHAT COMES IN BETWEEN (0-79)

T	O
2	2
7	3
6	0
4	9
1	7
5	6
3	8
2	7
5	8
6	3

T	O

T	O
2	4
7	5
6	2
5	1
1	9
5	8
4	0
2	9
6	0
6	5

Date: ________________ Teacher's Signature: ________________

WRITE BACKWARD COUNTING (49-40)

T	O
4	9

T	O
4	9

Date: ____________________ Teacher's Signature: ____________________

MORE AND LESS

Count the number of Balls in the first box. Then draw a group of balls that has more in the second box.

Count the number of Candies in the first box. Then draw a group of candies that has less in the second box.

Date: ____________

Teacher's Signature: ____________

NUMBER NAME - THREE (3)

Three				

Date: ________________ Teacher's Signature: ________________

NUMBER NAME - FOUR (4)

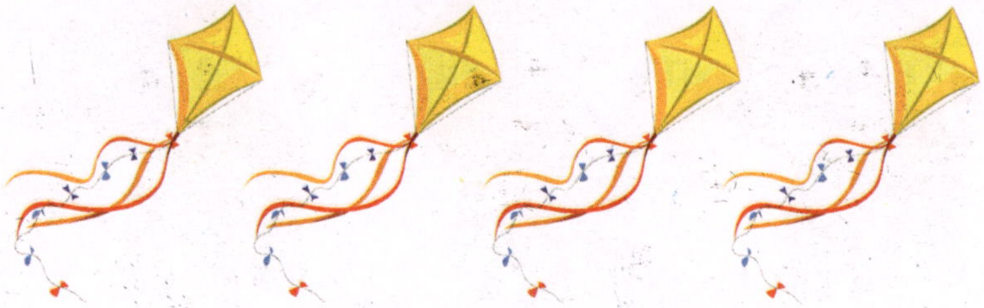

Four				

Date: ____________________

Teacher's Signature: ____________________

NUMBER NAME - FIVE (5)

Five				

Date: ________________ Teacher's Signature: ________________

WRITE FORWARD COUNTING (80-89)

T	O
8	0

T	O
8	0

Date: ____________________

Teacher's Signature: ____________________

WRITE FORWARD COUNTING (0-89)

0

Date: ________________ Teacher's Signature: ________________

WHAT COMES AFTER (0-89)

Write the numbers that come after.

Number	After	Number	After
54		87	
80		49	
21		35	
12		79	

Date: ____________ Teacher's Signature: ____________

WHAT COMES IN BETWEEN (0-89)

T	O	T	O	T	O
8	7			8	9
5	6			5	8
3	2			3	4
7	9			8	1
2	8			3	0
4	0			4	2
7	4			7	6
1	5			1	7
6	8			7	0
1	1			1	3

Date: ____________________ Teacher's Signature: ____________________

PUT <, = ,> (0-89)

78	◯	63	43	◯	43
50	◯	70	35	◯	59
9	◯	59	21	◯	52
71	◯	17	88	◯	81
22	◯	22	56	◯	66
57	◯	47	89	◯	89

Date: ________________

Teacher's Signature: ________________

NUMBER NAMES

Write the number names for each number.

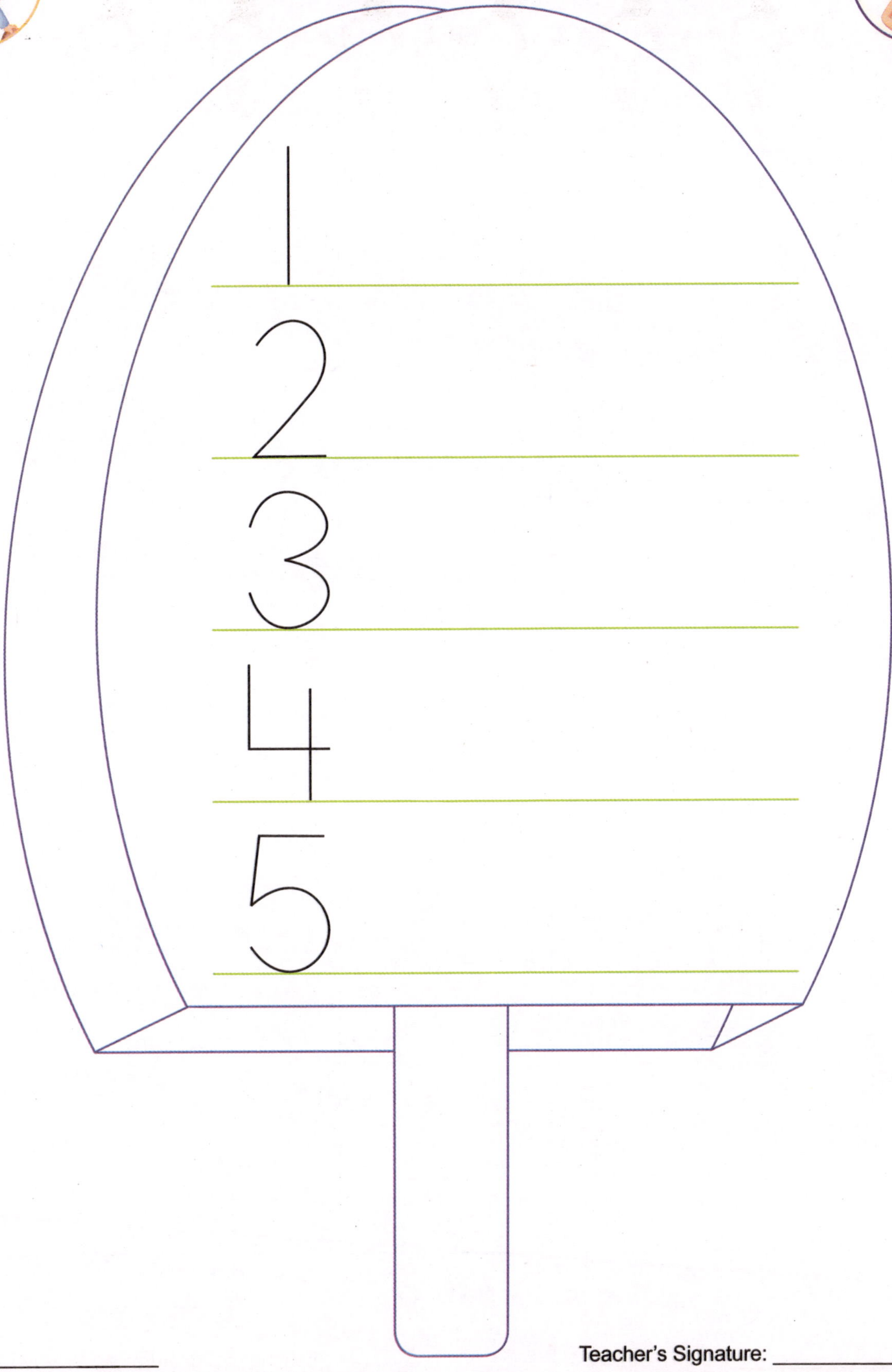

Date: ________________

Teacher's Signature: ________________

NUMBER NAME - SIX (6)

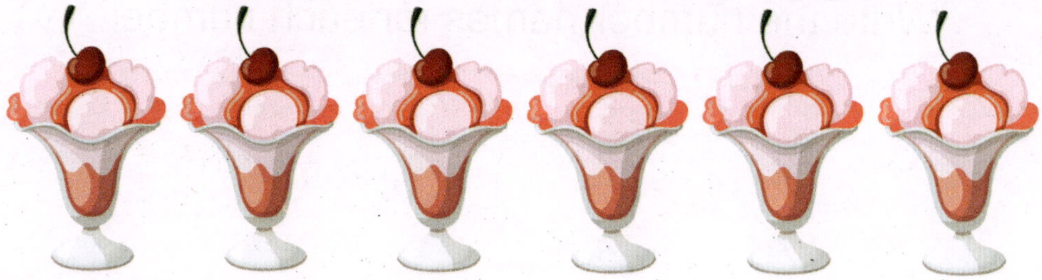

Six				

Date: ________________ Teacher's Signature: ________________

NUMBER NAME - SEVEN (7)

Seven				

Date: ____________________ Teacher's Signature: ____________________

WRITE FORWARD COUNTING (90-99)

T	O
9	0

T	O
9	0

Date: ____________________

Teacher's Signature: ____________________

WRITE FORWARD COUNTING (0-99)

0												

Date: ____________________ Teacher's Signature: ____________________

WHAT COMES AFTER (0-99)

Write the numbers that come after.

Number	After	Number	After
88		57	
92		8	
75		96	
17		34	

Date: ____________ Teacher's Signature: ____________

MISSING NUMBERS (0-99)

Fill in the missing numbers in correct order.

0				4					9
		12				16			
	21								
					35			38	
40			43				47		
				54					
		62							69
70								78	
		82	83						89
	91			94					

Date: ________________ Teacher's Signature: ________________

WHAT COMES IN BETWEEN (0-99)

T	O
7	0
5	9
9	2
9	7
8	5
9	4
5	8
1	3
2	8
3	1

T	O

T	O
7	2
6	1
9	4
9	9
8	7
9	6
6	0
1	5
3	0
3	3

Date: ____________________ Teacher's Signature: ____________________

ADDITION

These are 3 ice creams. Draw 2 more ice creams by tracing on the dotted lines. Now how many ice creams are there? Add and write the number.

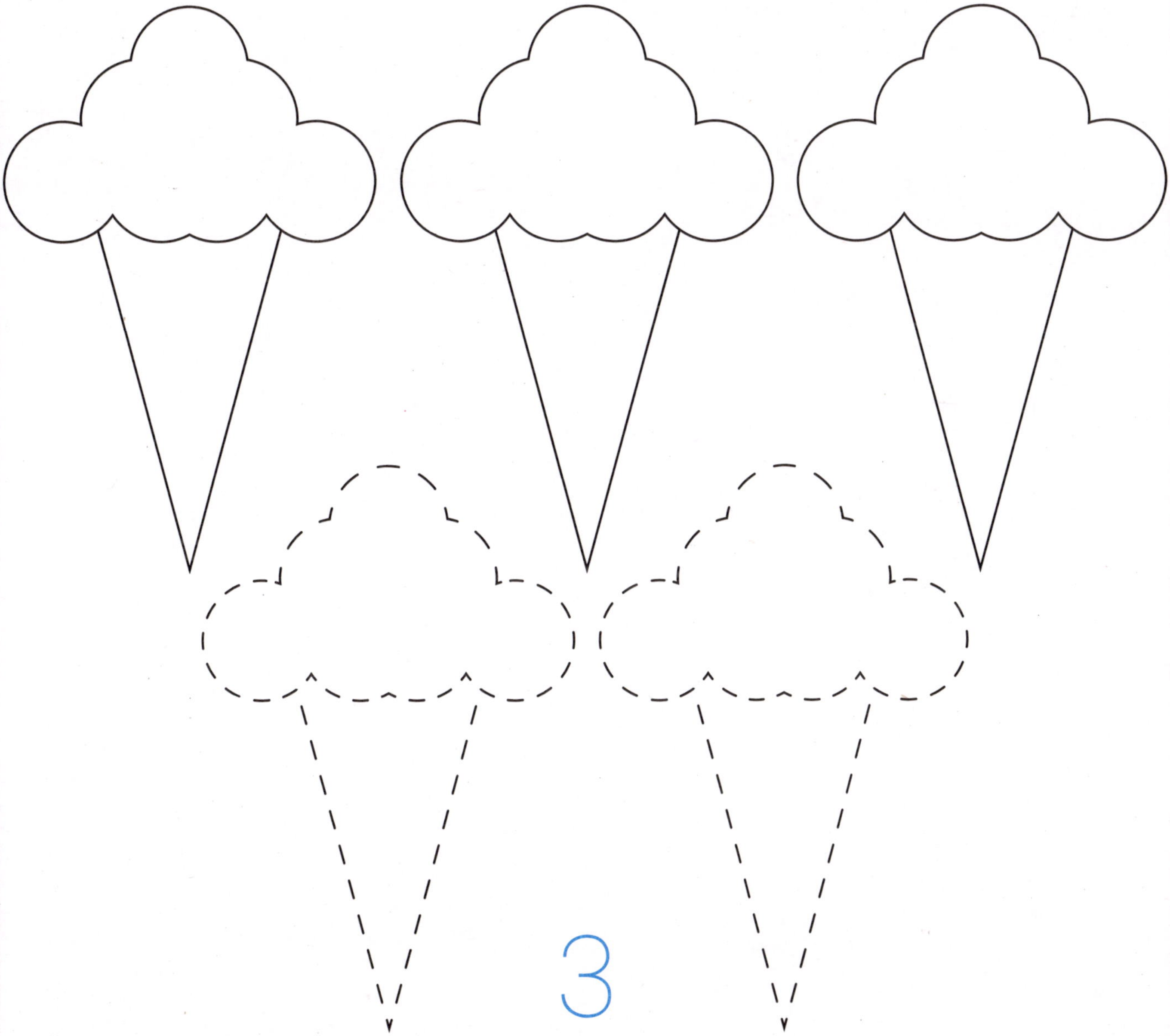

$$\begin{array}{r} 3 \\ +2 \\ \hline \\ \hline \end{array}$$

Date: ____________________ Teacher's Signature: ____________________

ADDITION

Write the sum in the orange colour below each addition problem.

1	4	3	2	6
+2	+3	+2	+7	+3

1	4	1	5	1
+7	+0	+1	+2	+4

2	3	2	3	1
+4	+1	+7	+5	+8

Date: ______________

Teacher's Signature: ______________

SUBTRACTION FUN

Look at the number of shapes in each row below and subtract the numbers. Write your answer in the given blank shapes.

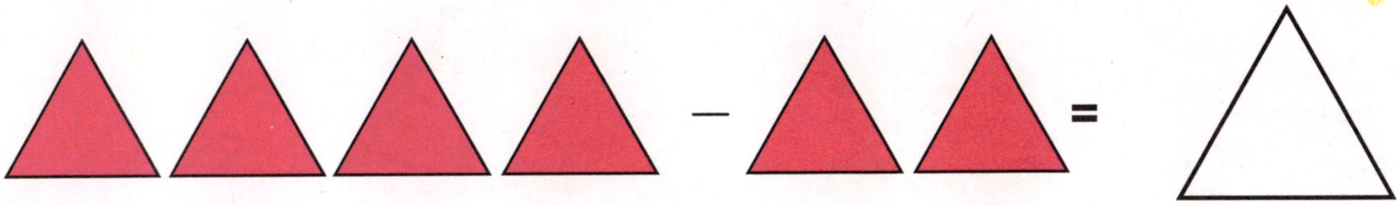

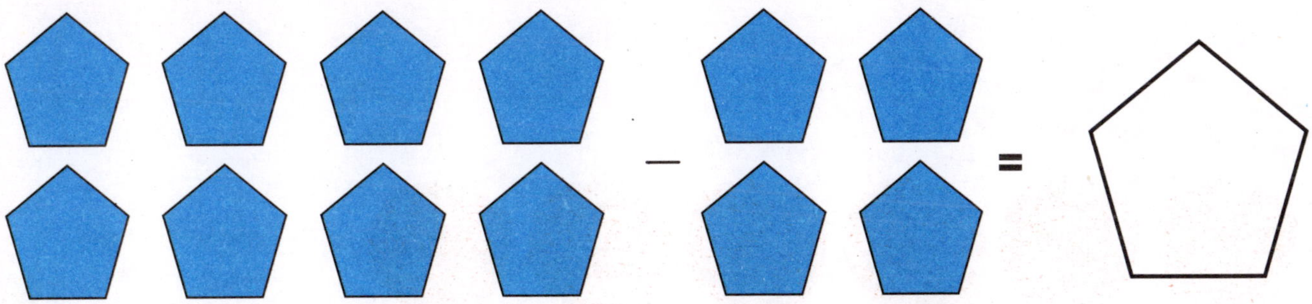

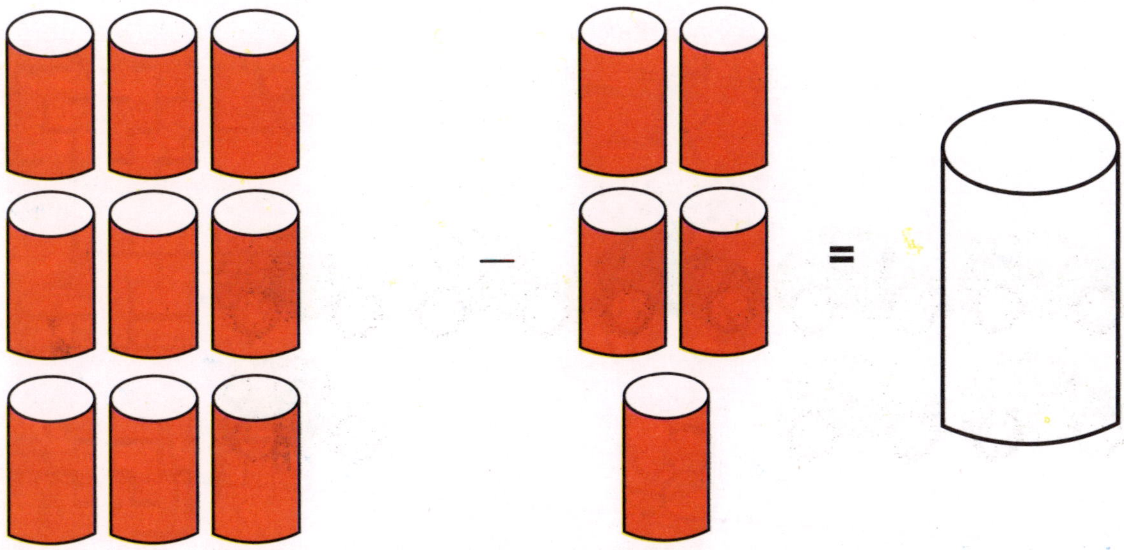

Date: ________________ Teacher's Signature: ________________

SUBTRACTION

Subtract and write the answer in the given box.

3 - 1 = ☐

6 - 2 = ☐

5 - 3 = ☐

8 - 7 = ☐

Date: ____________

Teacher's Signature: ____________

SUBTRACT AND ADD

Subtract and write the answer in the given box and colour the water animals to match the answers in the code below.

2 = blue   4 = green

3 = red   5 = yellow

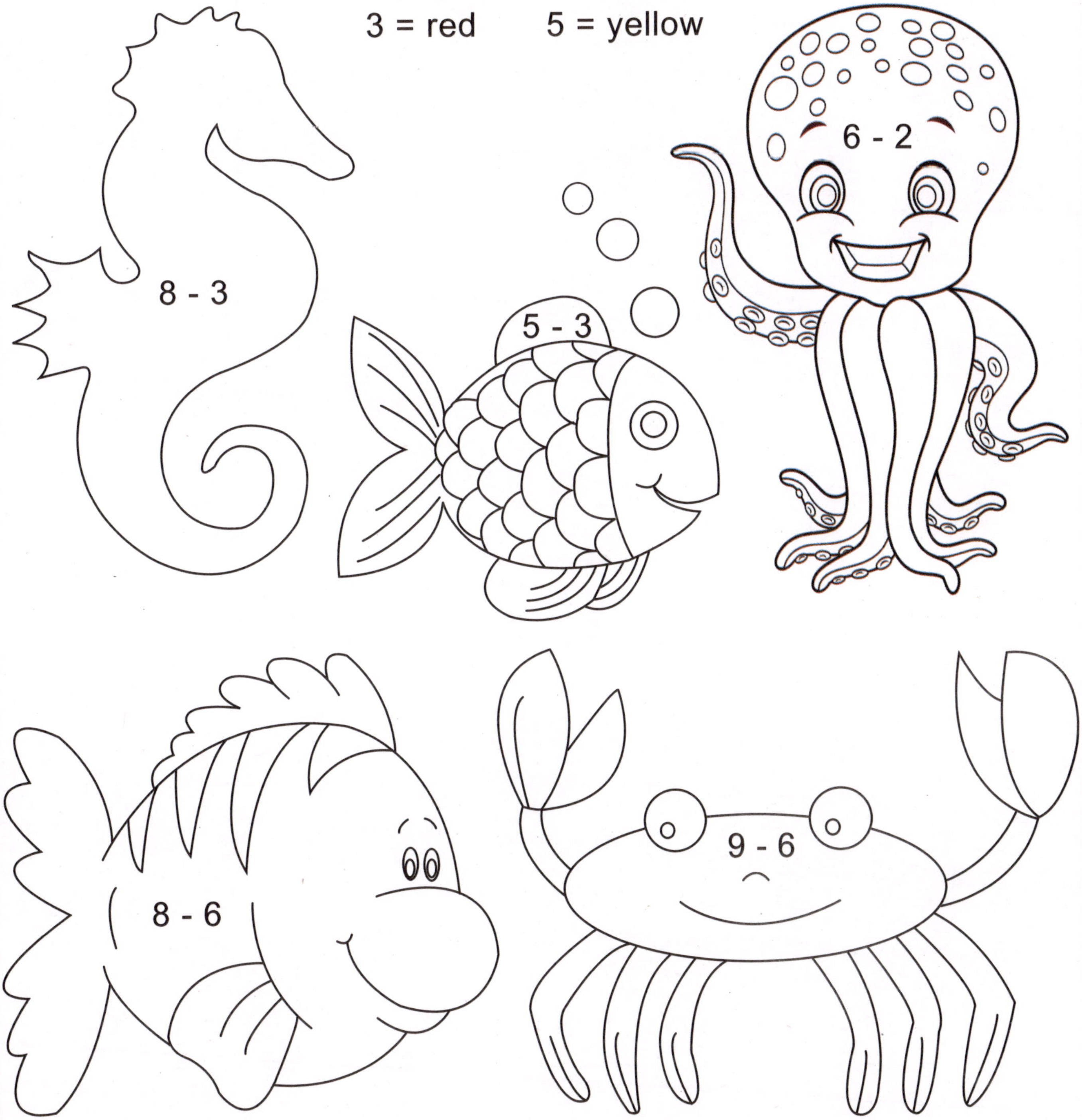

Date: ________________   Teacher's Signature: ________________

NUMBER NAME - EIGHT (8)

Eight				

Date: ____________________

Teacher's Signature: ____________________

NUMBER NAME - NINE (9)

Nine				

Date: ____________________ Teacher's Signature: ____________________

NUMBER NAME - TEN (10)

Ten				

Date: ________________   Teacher's Signature: ________________

NUMBER NAMES

Write the number names for each number.

6 ____________________

7 ____________________

8 ____________________

9 ____________________

10 ____________________

Date: ____________________ Teacher's Signature: ____________________

GREATER THAN / LESS THAN / EQUAL TO

Count the objects and write the numbers.
Then put the > or < or = symbol in the circle.

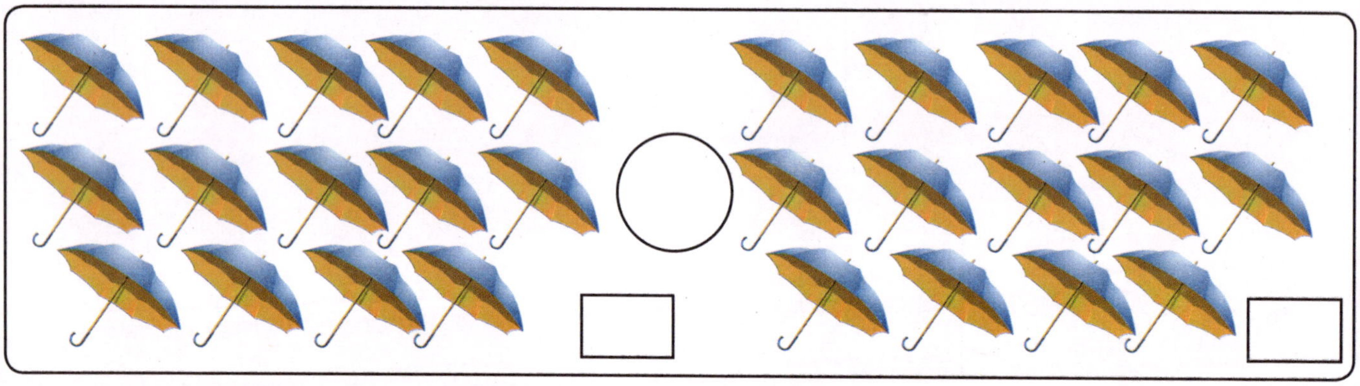

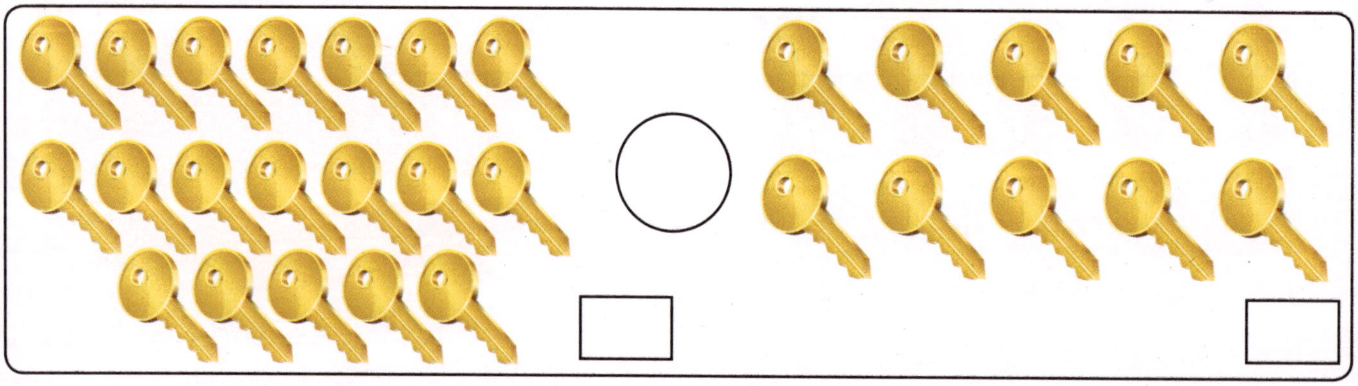

Date: ________________ Teacher's Signature: ________________

HOW MANY FRUITS!

Count the fruits in each box. Write number and number names for each fruit.

Date: ________________ Teacher's Signature: ________________

COLOURING FUN!

Pick up your crayons and colour the numbers below.

Date: ____________________

Teacher's Signature: ____________________